This book belongs to

....

The Summer Queen

Nick and Claire Page

Illustrations by Elena Baboni

make
believe
ideas

The Queen of Summer Island loved the sun.
People thought she loved sunshine more
than she loved the king or her four sons.
She never did any work. A young maid
looked after the children and taught them
all about the rain and the sun, the wind
and the clouds. (Some said she gave the
boys magic powers.)

The king would stroll around the island in the cool evening, helping people with their problems. When he didn't know the answers, he would ask the Moon for wisdom.

Sometimes it rained on Summer Island. Huge drops burst like bullets on the roofs. Rivers ran down the leaves of the banana trees.

The Summer Queen hated the rain.
She hated carrying an umbrella.
And she never splashed in puddles.

One day, after a long, lazy spell of sunshine, some rain clouds appeared. The people were glad: they needed water for their crops. But the Summer Queen was boiling mad!

"How do I get rid of these
rotten rainclouds?" she asked.
"Your sons can do it," whispered
a servant. The queen was amazed!

"Can my boys blow the clouds away?" she asked the young maid.
The maid replied: "Sun, rain, wind and snow;
I have taught them all I know,
If they blow the clouds, they'll go."
"Hot-diggity-dog!" exclaimed the queen. **"I can get rid of the rain forever!"**
But the maid said:
"Sun, snow, wind and rain,
They are young to stand such strain;
This will cause them too much pain."
"Don't care!" said the queen, selfishly.
"My children will do what I want."

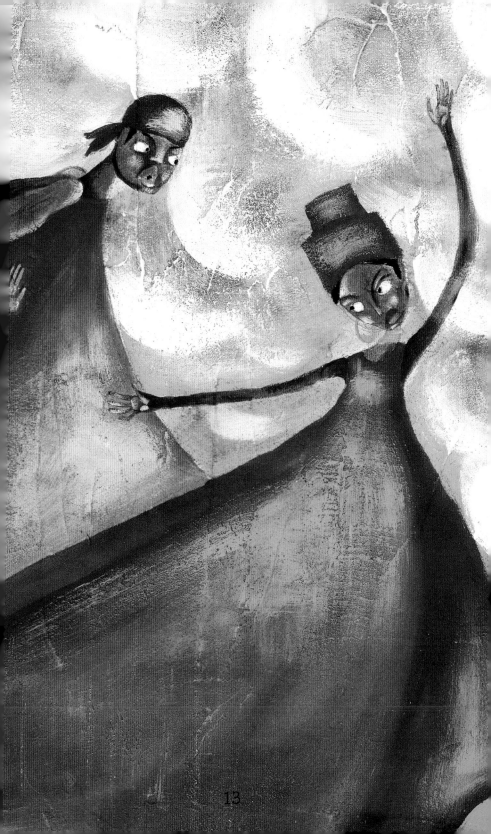

She took them to a high mountain.
"Blow the clouds away forever,"
she ordered.
"We can't do that!" they said.
"The island needs rain."
**"If you really loved me,
you'd do it!"** shouted the queen.

Because the boys really loved their mother, they faced north, south, east and west and started to blow...
The clouds slowly moved.
"Harder!" yelled the queen.
"That's not enough!"

So they blew harder, but now they
were very tired indeed.

"Harder!" said the queen.

"I thought you loved me!"

The boys gave one final puff and
the clouds disappeared.

"Sun-tastic!" cried the queen.
She did not notice that her boys
had fainted. She rushed back to
the royal sun lounger,
while the young maid
sent for a nurse.

After that, things got very bad.
There was no water for the island.
The crops began to die.
The soil turned to dust.

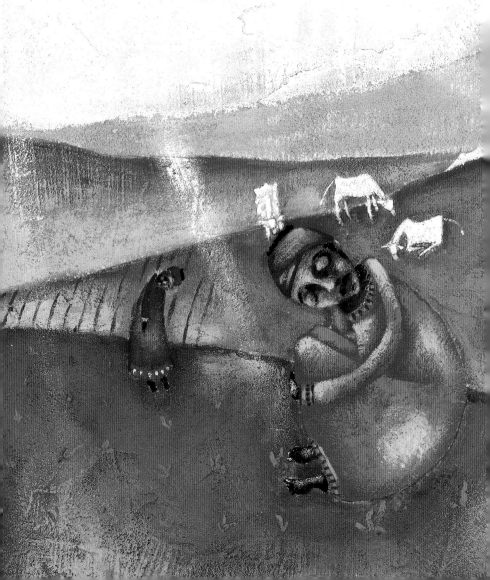

One day, while sunbathing, the queen called for a drink.

Instead of water, she was handed a glass of dry, red dust! She turned to find the king standing there.

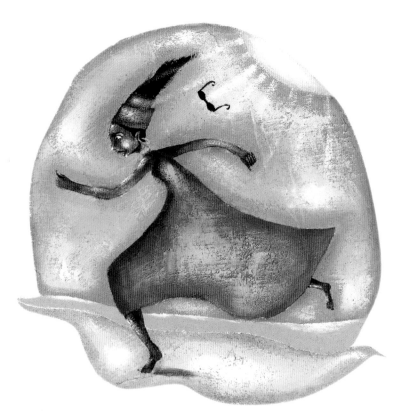

"What's this, you lunatic?" asked
the queen.

"The water has gone. The earth has turned
to dust," he said. "The Moon told me you
forced our sons to send the clouds away.
Now they are dying."

Suddenly, the queen's hot heart turned icy
cold. She rushed to their bedside. Their faces
were as white as the sand on the beach.

"What have I done!" cried the queen.
And the young maid said:
"Sun, rain, wind and snow;
Love will come and love will go.
Four boys lost, with just one blow."
The queen realised that she had been
living a selfish, dried-up life.
And she began to cry.

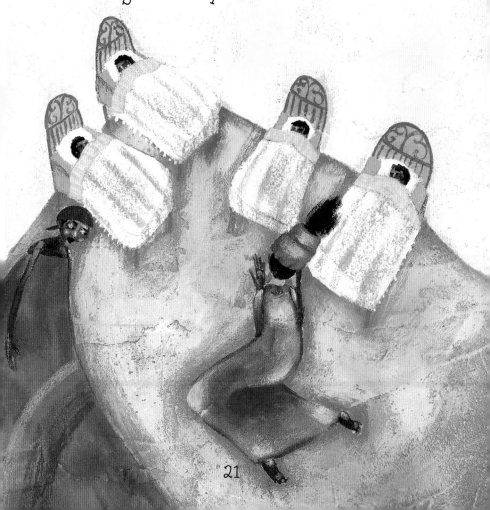

The queen cried so much, her tears flowed like rain, out of the door, along the streets and into the fields. They watered the crops and washed away the dust. They splashed onto her sons' faces and at once the boys awoke.

"I am so sorry!" she cried, hugging each one.

22

The maid picked some sugar cane and
made straws. She gave them to the boys
who sucked the clouds back towards
the island. The clouds grew bigger and
blacker until a storm broke.

Everyone danced in the rain.
Even the queen splashed in puddles.
Nobody noticed that the young maid
had gone. But later, over the island,
for the first time since anyone could
remember, there was
a rainbow.

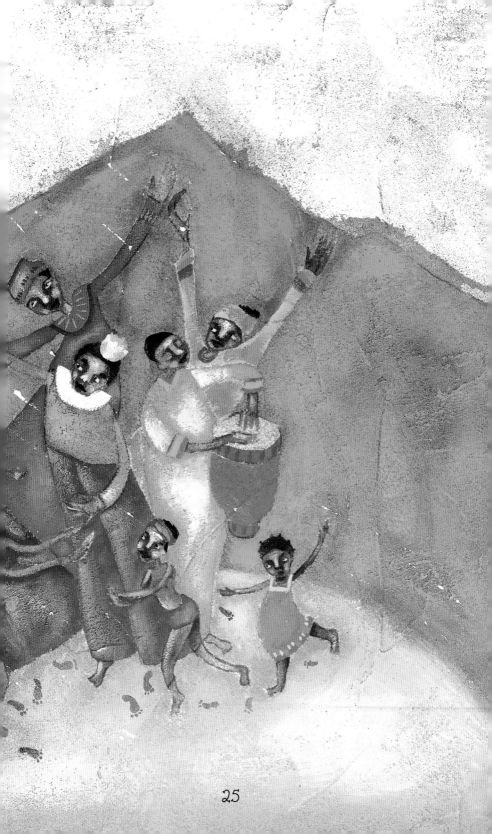

Ready to tell

Oh no! Some of the pictures from this story have been mixed up! Can you retell the story and point to each picture in the correct order?

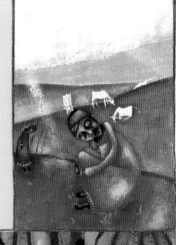

27

Picture dictionary

Encourage your child to read these harder
words from the story and gradually develop
their basic vocabulary.

beach   blow   clouds

drink   island   lazy

moon   rainbow   umbrella

Key words

Here are some key words used in context.
Help your child to use other words from
the border in simple sentences.

This child is small.

It rained all **day**.

The maid **can** help.

The boys **are** tired.

The sun **is** shining.

Brighten up your boots

The Summer Queen must have needed some very special royal wellies when she discovered what fun it was to dance in the rain. You, too, can make your boots fit for a queen by brightening them up with colourful stickers. Get out in those puddles and make a splash on a rainy day!

You will need

a pair of plain Wellington boots • lots of stickers • coloured insulation tape • scissors

What to do

1 You must make sure your boots are clean. Give them a good wash and leave them to dry (or rub them dry with some paper towels).

2 If you want to make stripes, ask a grown-up to cut some lengths of coloured insulation tape. Take care not to stick the strips of tape together!

3 Now you're ready to start sticking the tape and stickers on the boots. (It's probably best to decorate only the legs of the wellies, otherwise the stickers might wash off when you walk through puddles.) You can make neat patterns or just arrange the stickers higgledy-piggledy – it's up to you.

And that's all there is to it! Soon you'll have the brightest, most colourful, boots in town!